Race Day

By Olivia Suez

Illustrated by Ariel Pang

Target Skill Consonants Vv/v/ and Zz/z/

PEARSON

Scott
Foresman

Bev is in a green vest.

Vin is in a blue vest.

Vin will hop fast.

Get set, Vin.

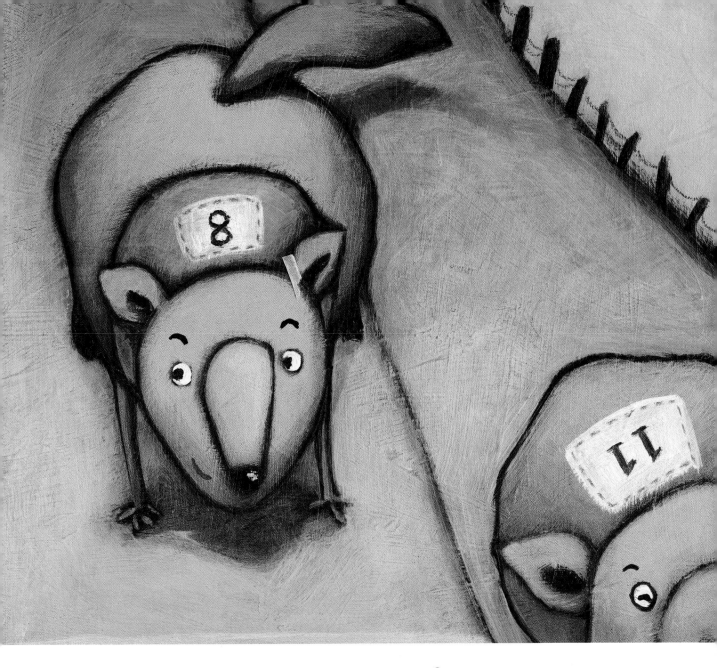

Bev will hop fast.

Get set, Bev.

Get set and go, Bev and Vin!
Look at Bev zip!

Hop, Bev and Vin, hop.
Look at Vin zip!

Bev and Vin can hop.

They hop fast.

Bev and Vin win!